easijazz

Published by
Chester Music
part of The Music Sales Group
14-15 Berners Street,
London W1T 3LJ, UK.

Exclusive Distributors:
Music Sales Limited
Distribution Centre, Newmarket Road,
Bury St Edmunds, Suffolk IP33 3YB, UK.
Music Sales Corporation
257 Park Avenue South,
New York, NY 10010, USA.
Music Sales Pty Limited
20 Resolution Drive, Caringbah,
NSW 2229, Australia.

Order No. CH77396
ISBN 978-1-84938-820-7

Edited by Oliver Miller.
Cover design by Ruth Keating.

Original compositions by John Kember.
Piano – John Kember.

Printed in the EU.

Your Guarantee of Quality
As publishers, we strive to produce every book to the
highest commercial standards.
This book has been carefully designed to minimise awkward
page turns and to make playing from it a real pleasure.
Particular care has been given to specifying acid-free, neutral-sized paper
made from pulps which have not been elemental chlorine bleached.
This pulp is from farmed sustainable forests and was
produced with special regard for the environment.
Throughout, the printing and binding have been planned to
ensure a sturdy, attractive publication which should give years of enjoyment.
If your copy fails to meet our high standards,
please inform us and we will gladly replace it.

www.chesternovello.com

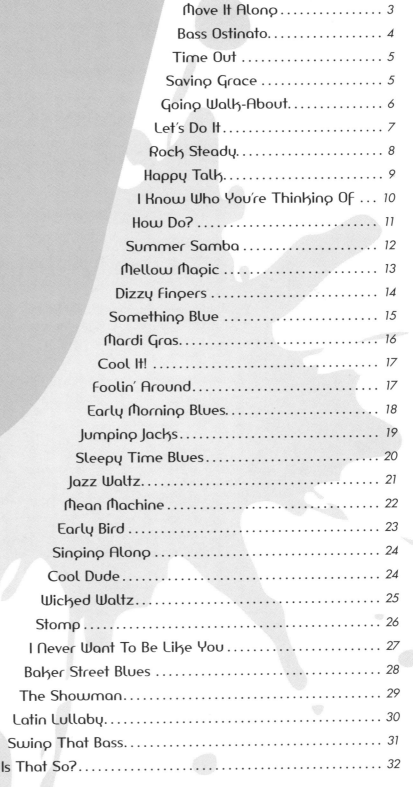

Wise Publications
part of The Music Sales Group
London / New York / Paris / Sydney / Copenhagen / Berlin / Madrid / Hong Kong / Tokyo

easijazz

This collection of 34 easy pieces for piano solo began as an attempt to make this popular genre available to relative beginners on the piano, and for pianists at primary and intermediate levels.

My wish is that these pieces will enable them to experience the pleasure of playing in an authentic sounding jazz style as soon as possible.

The pieces presented are in a wide range of styles including Latin and rock in addition to the more familiar 'swing' style of playing.

Together these pieces will introduce the pianist to the rhythmic discipline required and help to develop a strong sense of coordination while enjoying the challenges and opportunities of performing short and varied pieces.

John Kember

Tips On Style And Performance

1. Make it a habit always to 'count in' before you begin to play – keeping a steady pulse is essential in all styles and can only be relaxed when playing a more expressive Ballad. The convention in jazz is a 2 bar count in:

   1 – 2 – 1 2 3 4

   which is ideal for Latin and rock numbers which always have even quavers

   When playing in a 'swing' style the difference is indicated as:

   a1 – a2 – a1 2 3 4

2. To achieve an authentic jazz 'feel' to your playing try to 'lean on' or gently accent notes that are tied, particularly those which anticipate the third or first beats of the bar. Better still try to lighten the preceding note by playing it slightly short, but in time.

3. Staccato notes rarely need to be accented. Those that end a short phrase should be light and crisp, and should be similar to the effect of a high-hat cymbal struck in the closed position – a sort of "tch" sound of no duration. This is made even more effective if the preceding note is slightly accented.

4. Playing in any jazz style is all about rhythm, so always work at this before you play any of the notes. Again the conventional way (and it is more fun too) is to vocalise the rhythms using "bah-doo-bah-doo" type sounds!

I Know Where I'm Going

- The title should give you an indication of how to play the first phrase 'I-know-where-I'm-go-ing'
- Give the quaver groups an easy 'swing' feel
- In five-note position in each hand. The right-hand third finger will play both A and A♭

Move It Along

- A crisp and light staccato is desirable to give the piece its character
- Swing the four-quaver groups – 'move-it-a-long' – but play the fourth quaver very lightly and short

Bass Ostinato

- The two-bar left-hand phrase is repeated, only changing in bars 7–8 and 15–16
- Both hands should be in five-note positions but with the right hand an octave higher in the second half

Moderato (even quavers)

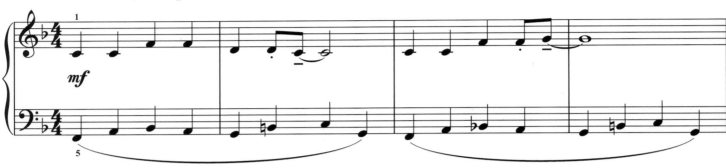

Time Out

- The unusual feature of this piece is the empty bars, which means that the time will need to be counted steadily
- Keep the staccato notes short, and light in touch – think of the sound a hi-hat cymbal makes when struck in a closed position

Saving Grace

- Although only five notes are played by each hand, the rhythms are more varied than in previous pieces
- Play the grace notes at the same time as the left-hand notes and not before
- You will find it useful to practise the opening bar as a rhythm first by clapping or tapping, but make sure that the quaver is unaccented and played just before the third beat

Going Walk-About

- As the title suggests, the left-hand bass line 'walks', evenly, steadily and legato, with a two-bar, five-finger repeated pattern
- The right hand stays in a five-note shape but with the second finger playing D♯ and the third finger playing E♭ as necessary
- Keeping a steady left-hand beat is essential, and practice will be necessary in order to keep the independence of a steady left hand and a 'swinging' right hand

Let's Do It

- Here is a simple rhythm that fits the title, and all in a five-note position – with the right hand an octave higher midway

Moderato (even quavers)

Rock Steady

- Apart from the three bars that contain quavers this piece uses mainly crotchets, and hands remain in their five-note positions
- This should be played quite firmly (*pesante*) but will benefit from clear dynamic contrasts

Rhythmic (even quavers)

Happy Talk

- This piece remains in the same five-note positions throughout, the only deviation being a single F♮ in the left hand
- Here is a pattern of repeated notes followed by the anticipation of the first beat

Giocoso (even quavers)

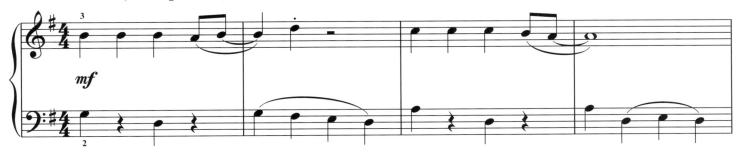

Know Who You're Thinking Of

- You do not need to swing this piece as | ♩ ♫ ♫ ♩ | is found a great deal in Latin style music
- To play in a really authentic way, lighten the first quaver of a group and 'lean' on the second (tied) one
- Watch the fingering carefully as there are a number of changes and more than five notes in each hand

Moderato (even quavers)

How Do?

- Both hands extend to six notes
- The repeated crotchets in the left hand will help to keep a constant beat, and give a simple 'rock' beat to the piece
- Make sure that the anticipated third beat does not unsettle the left hand
- The *D.C.* (Da Capo) means to repeat from the beginning and stop at the *Fine*

Vivace (even quavers)

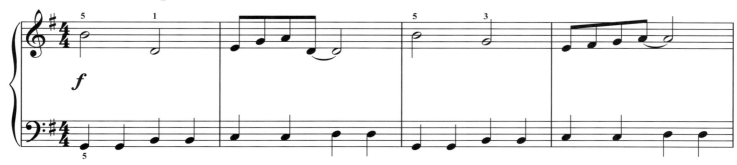

Fine

D.C. al Fine

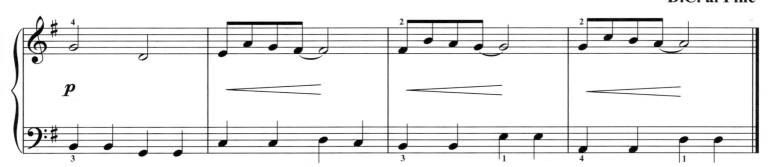

- Another Latin American dance style, this time without any syncopation but instead using simple rhythms to provide its character

Giocoso (even quavers)

Mellow Magic

- A gentle swing piece with anticipation of both first and third beats
- In a single position to begin with but with some variation (indicated by the fingering) and a repeat

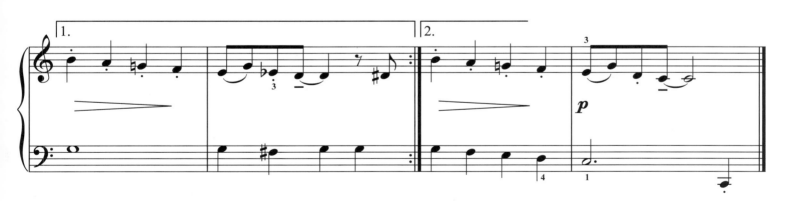

zy fingers

- Here is another piece that needs to be played with a relaxed swing feel to the right-hand quavers
- Both hands remain in a five-note position with a change indicated midway

Something Blue

- The frequent changes from B♭ (A♯) and B♮ provide the 'blues' effect, but by use of chords C7 and G, rather than changes of tonality

Mardi Gras

- You will find some movement and changes of position in both hands in this piece, so it is advisable to learn each hand separately first
- Notice the anticipated right-hand quavers which occur on the third beat in alternate bars, and make sure the left hand remains on the beat
- As with all Latin styles, the quavers are played evenly

Bright Latin

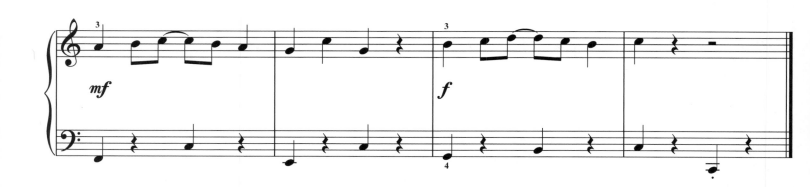

Cool It!

- The left-hand 'walking bass' repeats three times, but watch out for where the figure changes in bar 8
- Make the right hand sound really mean – think 'cool it!' and make the 'it' both short and light in touch

Foolin' Around

- The title here helps to establish the rhythm of the chromatic four-note figures in the right hand – 'fool-in'-a-round' – while the left hand remains in a five-note shape throughout
- Notice the frequent changes of position required in the right hand

Early Morning Blues

- All right-hand quavers need a relaxed 'swing' feel i.e. played in a similar way to quavers in 6/8: ♩ ♪ ♩ ♪ ♩ ♪ ♪ ↾ |
- Where a short phrase ends with a staccato quaver (bar 1, bar 2, etc.), make it a light staccato without any trace of an accent
- Any accent should be on the quaver preceding one with a staccato, for an authentic jazz feel
- 'Swing' quavers should always be relaxed (lazy) and never sound clipped or rigid

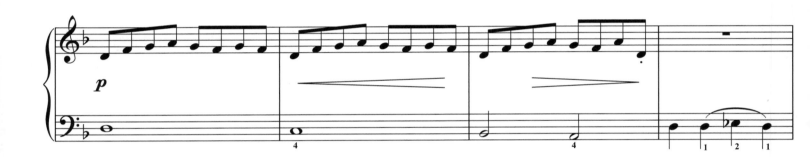

Jumping Jacks

- This piece should have a sense of energy and bounce – staccato crotchets and crisp rhythms will help achieve this
- Again it is the third beat anticipation that gives the piece its character, whether it is | ♩. ♪ - | or | ♪♪♪♪. - |, and a natural swing to all quavers

19

Sleepy Time Blues

- Both hands stay in a five-note position but with the third finger of the right hand playing both E and E♭ and the second finger D and D♯
- The rhythm │ ♩ ♫ ♫ ♩ ♩ │ is used extensively
- In bar 3 the second beat is anticipated and then the first of bar 4 – watch out for similar rhythms throughout the piece

20

Jazz Waltz

- The 'jazz waltz' rhythm occurs in both hands but mainly in the left
- Syncopated and even bars alternate
- Clap this left-hand rhythm until it feels natural and comfortable before you play

21

Mean Machine

- Like all Latin styles, rock uses only even quavers
- Keep the beat steady and the phrase endings short and crisp – but never accented
- Don't get caught out by the rhythmic change in bar 6

Moderate 'rock' feel

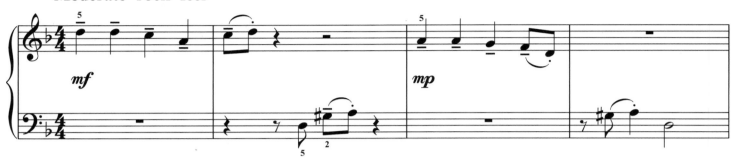

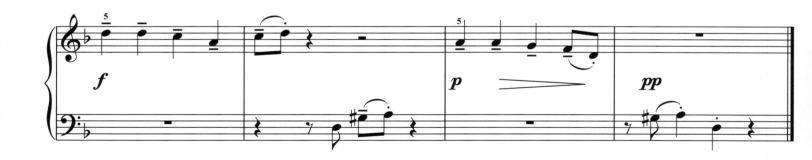

Early Bird

- There is just a hint of syncopation in the left hand throughout
- Ensure that the melody 'sings out' clearly and smoothly

Jazz waltz feel

Singing Along

- Another piece in which the quaver groups need a 'long–short, long–short' swing feel
- The title will help with the four-quaver phrase which starts each alternate bar
- Again, this piece is in a five-note position with the right hand this time playing both B and B♭ with the third finger

Cool Dude

- It is worth getting to know the rhythms before playing this piece – the dotted crotchet should be long and slightly accented, while the quaver needs to be short and light, and gone before the third count

Wicked Waltz

- The characteristic 'jazz waltz' rhythm is found in alternate bars, but also in both hands
- There is only limited movement in both hands but try to achieve an effective 'fade out' in the closing bars

Vivo

Stomp

- Based on a 12-bar framework this requires a solid, earthy, positive rhythm
- The right hand makes full use of grace notes and triplets, and in the final two bars plays from the bass clef, as indicated

I Never Want To Be Like You

- This piece begins easily enough as a simple swing piece
- The three repeated phrases at the end need clear dynamic contrasts to be effective
- A lively tempo is needed

Baker Street Blues

- The right hand is repetitive in both notes and rhythms, only changing position with changes in the harmony
- This piece follows a classic 12-bar blues pattern (see below) in C major and uses a constant walking bass line

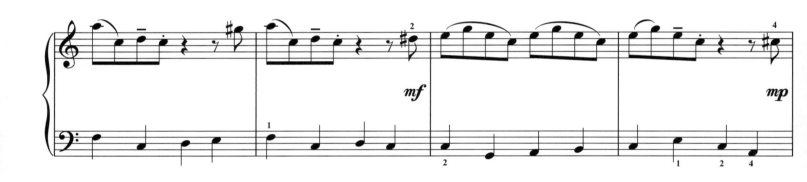

The Showman

- Reminiscent of a style often found in stage shows, the melody is made up using four basic and related rhythms, anticipating either the third or first beats of the bar

Latin Lullaby

- To achieve the right feel or 'groove' you need to think in eights – that is eight quaver beats in each bar – then accent, tap and play the first, fourth and seventh quavers
- Play this piece slowly to begin with, then build up to a moderate, but not fast, tempo

Moderato (even quavers)

Swing That Bass

- A repeated two-bar bass figure runs throughout; it is advisable to get to know this well on its own before attempting to add the right-hand melody
- You may find some of the coordination a little tricky

Is That So?

- There is something of the style of a Hollywood 'Western' film in this left-hand figure with its easy swing and extended twelve-bar pattern
- It will help to understand the underlying chord structure, in the key of F major:

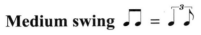

```
|  C7  |  C7  |  F7  |  F7  |
|  C7  |  C7  |  C7  |  C7  |
|  Bb7 |  Bb7 |  F   |  F   |
|  C7  |  Bb7 |  F   |  F   |
```